OH, BROTHER! OH, SISTER!

Written By Phyllis Halloran
Illustrated By Kathryn E. Shoemaker

The Reading Well Series

Milliken Publishing Company, St. Louis, Missouri

For my brother Bernard, with love.
P.H.

For Kristin and her brother, Andrew.
K.E.S.

© 1989 by Milliken Publishing Company

Series Editors: Patricia and Fredrick McKissack
Cover Design by Graphcom, Inc., St. Louis, Missouri
Logo Design by Justmann Associates, St. Louis, Missouri

Library of Congress Catalog Card Number: 88-60392
ISBN 0-88335-767-4 (pbk.) / ISBN 0-88335-788-7 (lib. bdg.)

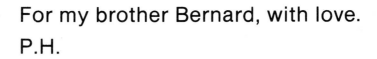

Some Surprise!

You're not a puppy.
You're not a cat.

You're a little baby
in a funny little hat.

I wanted a puppy.
I wanted a cat.
I got a little baby.
And that is that!

Baby Sister Blues

This is my new sister.
She's small and looks so sweet.
Well, she can't walk or talk yet,
and there's not much she will eat.

She smiles and makes big bubbles
and has two teeth to bite.
But what she does the very best
is cry and cry all night.

Just Me

Once upon a time,
I was the only one.
Now there is you,
and it's not much fun!

Someday

When you were small,
did you do the things I do?
When I grow up,
do you think I'll look like you?

Trouble

What is this?
What did you do?
I can't wait
to tell on you!

Why?

Why do you play with my stuff
when you have so much of your own?

I wish you would play with your stuff
and leave all of mine alone.

Let's Read

Come over here, and we will look
at all the things in my new book.

See the truck and the big, red ball.
Look at the cat upon the wall.

Soon you'll grow, then you will **see**
what fun it can be reading to me.

Not Needed

We are big now.
Stop the fuss!
We don't need you
watching us!

13

Hurry!

I'm tired of being at the end.
I'm tired of being last.

I hope Mom has that baby,
and I hope she has it fast.

Middle Child

One of us is big.
One of us is little.
I'm the one who fits
right in the middle.

Enough!

Do you have to do what I do?
Do you have to say what I say?
Do you have to go where I go?
Can't you just go away?

17

How Come?

With you I'm always happy.
With you I'm never sad.

How come when you're with me
I always make you mad?

The Best

You wash the dishes
that I have to dry.

You make the kites
that I like to fly.

You help with homework
that's hard to do.

There's not another brother
in the world like you.

You'll Be Sorry

I'm going to get you!
You will see.
Then you'll be sorry
you told on me.

23

Yikes!

Let's stay up and talk tonight
after we have to turn off the light.

24

25

We can tell stories out loud
in the dark about monsters,
giants, and a great big shark.

Then when we're both as scared as can be,
we'll dive for the covers — one, two, three!

Never Alone

On a dark and windy night
when the moon hangs in the tree,
I am just so very glad
that you are sleeping here with me.

Vocabulary

a	come	good	like	only	stuff	wait
about	covers	got	little	or	surprise	walk
after	cry	great	look	our	sweet	wall
all	dark	grow	loud	out	talk	want
alone	did	hangs	mad	over	teeth	was
always	dishes	happy	make(s)	own	tell	wash
am	dive	hard	me	play	that	watc
and	do	has	middle	puppy	the	we
are	does	hat	mine	read	then	we'll
as	doesn't	have	mom	reading	there	we're
at	don't	help	monsters	red	thing(s)	what
away	dry	here	moon	right	this	wher
baby	eat	homework	much	sad	three	wher
ball	end	hope	my	say	time	who
be	enough	how	need	scared	tired	why
being	fast	hurry	needed	see	to	will
best	fits	I	never	shark	told	wind
big	fly	I'm	new	she	tonight	wish
bite	for	in	night	sister	tree	with
blues	fun	is	no	small	trouble	worl
book	funny	it	not	smiles	truck	woul
both	fuss	just	now	so	turn	yet
brother	get	kites	of	soon	two	yikes
bubbles	giants	last	off	sorry	up	you
can	glad	leave	on	stay	upon	you'
can't	go	let	once	stop	us	you'r
cat	going	light	one	stories	very	your
child